This SPECIAL STORIES BOOK Belongs To:

_____

Distributor: Irish Deaf.com
1st Floor
386 North Circular Road
Dublin 7
www.irishdeaf.com
Fax: +353-1-4846449
Text only: +353-85-7263511

Text copyright © Kate Gaynor, 2009

Illustrations copyright © Karen Quirke, 2009

Published in 2009 by
Special Stories Publishing

Member of CLÉ – The Irish Book Publishers Association

Designed by Graham Thew Design www.grahamthew.com

ISBN 978 0 9561751 3 7

A catalogue record for this book is available from the British Library

Printed by C&C Offset Printing Co, Ltd, China

 Special Stories Publishing
www.specialstories.ie

A BIRTHDAY FOR
BEN

By Kate Gaynor

Illustrated by Karen Quirke

Hi! My name is Ben and last week was my 7th birthday. When you meet me for the first time you might notice I'm wearing something on my ear.

Before you ask, it's not for listening to music or for talking on the phone. It's to help me with my hearing!

Some people can find everyday things difficult to do. My friend Sam finds it hard to see, so he wears glasses to help him see more clearly. I'm deaf, which means I don't hear very well, so I wear a hearing aid to help me to hear.

Even though I have a hearing aid, I still find it hard to
hear clearly some of the the words that people are saying.
Because of this, the way I speak might sound a little
different to my friends.

When I'm with my friends they try not to speak too fast. It sometimes helps if I watch their lips carefully so that I can understand what they are saying.

I have lots of other friends who are not in my school who also wear hearing aids. When we are together we sometimes use a special language called sign language which means using our hands instead of our voices to communicate with each other.

Even people who don't wear hearing aids use their hands to make themselves understood. Like when you wave to your friend to say hello or goodbye, or when a policeman needs to direct cars on the road.

Sometimes I feel a little bit different to my friends in school. Not because I find it hard to hear but because I don't really like birthday parties! When the time comes to play party games I feel left out. For a lot of the games you need to hear the music to be able to join in.

"Ben, you can't play because you won't be able to
hear the music," my friend Jim told me at his birthday party.
So I just sat by myself until the games were over and
it was time to go home.

One day when my Mum was driving me home from school,
she asked me if I'd like to have a party for my 7th birthday
and invite all of my friends along.

"No," I said angrily. "I hate birthday parties".
"Very well," said Mum with a smile, "No birthday for Ben this year".

On the morning of my 7th birthday my big sister Sophie
woke me up early so I could open my presents.
"Happy Birthday, Ben!" she shouted happily.
"Humph… I hate birthdays," I said.

Later that day I went for a drive with my Dad to the shops.
When we arrived home Dad opened the front door very
slowly and told me to go ahead inside.

"Surprise, Happy Birthday Ben!" everyone shouted.
All of my friends had party hats and were there
to surprise me and have a party for my birthday.

"Oh no," I whispered to Mum. "What party games will we play? I don't want my friends who are deaf to feel left out".

"Don't worry Ben," she said, "there are lots of games you can play where everyone can join in and have fun," said Mum.

First, we played pass the parcel. Everyone sat in a big circle
and passed around a present with lots of wrapping paper on
it. Instead of stopping the music to find out who the winner
would be, Mum flashed the lights so we all could
tell when to stop!

Next we played musical chairs. As well as playing the
music, Mum used red stop and green go cards to let
everyone know when to stop and find a chair and
when to start again.

Afterwards we all played a game of hide and seek in the garden. This time no one felt left out and we all joined in and had lots of fun together.

When it was time for my friends to go home they all said it
was the best birthday party they had ever been to! Now I
just can't wait for my next birthday, and I'd like to invite
you to come along too!

NOTES FOR GROWN UP'S:

A CHILD'S HEARING ability can be affected by congenital or genetic issues, head injuries, loud noise, infections or brain damage. Hearing loss can occur anywhere in the auditory (hearing) system. Mixed hearing loss is a combination of conductive and sensorineural hearing loss.

The two main types of hearing loss are:
1) Conductive Hearing Loss: This may be temporary and occurs when sound vibrations from the outer or middle ear are blocked from reaching the inner ear. Causes: fluid in the middle ear middle-ear infections, a perforated eardrum, earwax in the ear canal, unusual bone growth (otosclerosis), or head injury.
2) Sensorineural Hearing Loss: This is permanent and occurs in the pathway from the inner ear (including the cochlea) to the nerve fibres that link the inner ear to the brain for hearing. Causes: head injury, mumps, meningitis, congenital issues, acoustic trauma (loud noise), stroke, Meniere's disease, brain or auditory nerve tumour or multiple sclerosis.

HOW TO USE THIS BOOK:

CHILDREN WITH hearing issues may often feel different to their peers due to wearing hearing-aids. Or feel left behind in games or group situations that involve auditory exchanges. This story helps all children to see the difficulties that a child in this situation might face and how certain everyday situations might upset them. Through the main character, children who are deaf/hard of hearing also learn that it's OK to mention the specific frustrations and issues they experience. People around the children also become more aware of possible workarounds to communication issues or situations. The story helps to reinforce how important it is that no child is ever excluded or left out. Ben's story offers a broad introduction to the various challenges a child with hearing difficulties may face. As with any story however, this is only one interpretation of mainstream school and the experience of all deaf or hard of hearing children will differ depending on their environment, family background or personality.

IRISH DEAF KIDS (IDK) is a "for-impact" venture aimed at supporting inclusive education for deaf children in Ireland while empowering parents to develop their child's full potential.   For parents, educators / teachers, deaf people and others, IDK provides an interactive website and online forum for discussion and guidance on best practice for education. Over 2,000 deaf children currently attend mainstream schools in Ireland. Parents and teachers need to network and share ideas to ensure consistent educational standards. Early intervention and language acquisition are necessary for deaf children to have a mainstream education but parents and teachers in Ireland lack key reference points. This is where IDK comes in.

web: www.irishdeafkids.ie
http://forum.irishdeafkids.ie
email: info@irishdeafkids.ie

Acknowledgements:

Many thanks to the Special Stories Publishing advisory Board, Michael Gill, Sandra O'Malley, Aine Lynch, David Shaw, Fintan Maher, Paul Toner and to Social Entrepreneurs Ireland, Sean, Lynda, Claire and Annalisa for all of their encouragement, advice and unwavering support. Many thanks also to Kieran O'Donoghue, Michael & George Gaynor and our extended family and friends, Liam Gaynor, Liz O'Donoghue, Trevor Patterson and Karen Quirke, Mary Lindsay ISL, Eamon and Teresa Quirke, Graham Thew, James Fitzsimons, Louise Sheerin and the Irish Deaf Society and Dr. Lorraine Leeson at the Centre for Deaf Studies Trinity College Dublin

Special Stories Publishing is supported by Social Entrepreneurs Ireland
www.socialentrepreneurs.ie

Special thanks to Caroline Carswell from Irish Deaf Kids.ie without whose involvement this book would have not been possible.

Special thanks also to Dr. Imelda Coyne, Trinity College Dublin whose time and effort with this project was so greatly appreciated.

About the Author:

Kate Gaynor is the author of 11 published children's books. Her titles address the issues of children with special education needs or health and social problems. She works closely with healthcare professionals, psychologists, teachers and families on a daily basis to ensure the quality of her work. Kate is an English and Sociology graduate of University College Dublin and lives and works in Dublin, Ireland

About the Illustrator:

Karen Quirke was born in Dublin, Ireland and currently lives in Malahide, Co.Dublin. Karen was educated in St. Mary's School for Deaf Girls in Cabra, Co.Dublin and afterwards in Roslyn Park College. Karen's interests include sign language, illustration and photography.

Other Books from SPECIAL STORIES PUBLISHING
The SPECIAL STORIES SERIES 2:

THE SPECIAL STORIES SERIES 2 – These books are designed to introduce all children to the positive aspects of inclusive education with each book featuring a character with a certain special education need. The stories help children to learn the importance of accepting friends and classmates who are 'different' to them.

A BIRTHDAY FOR BEN

Children with hearing difficulties. It's Ben's 7th birthday, but he really doesn't want a birthday party! When his friends surprise him, he then learns just how easy it is for everyone to join in the fun.

TOM'S SPECIAL TALENT

Dyslexia/Learning difficulties. Tom isn't sure if he really has any talents at all when he sees how good his friends are at reading and writing. But a school competition helps him to find his own very 'special talent'.

FREDDIE'S SUPER SUMMER

Down Syndrome. It's Freddie's very first time at summer camp and he's certain he won't enjoy it or make friends. But it isn't long before a boy called Jerry helps him to see otherwise!

A FRIEND LIKE SIMON:

Autism/ASD. When a new boy joins Matthew's school, he's just not sure if he wants to have a friend like Simon. But a school trip to the funfair soon helps to change his mind!

(Books are sold separately and/or as part of a box set)

The SPECIAL STORIES SERIES 1:

A FAMILY FOR SAMMY
Foster Care

FIRST PLACE
Cleft Palate & Speech difficulties

THE LOST PUPPY
Limited mobility/ wheelchair users

THE FAMOUS HAT
Childhood Cancer

JOE'S SPECIAL STORY
Inter-country Adoption

THE WINNER
Asthma

THE BRAVEST GIRL IN SCHOOL
Diabetes

(Books are sold separately and/or as part of a box set)

www.specialstories.ie

www.specialstories.ie